Little

Written by Rozanne Lanczak Williams
Created by Sue Lewis
Illustrated by Patty Briles

Creative Teaching Press

Little Zebra
© 2002 Creative Teaching Press, Inc.
Written by Rozanne Lanczak Williams
Illustrated by Patty Briles
Project Manager: Sue Lewis
Project Director: Carolea Williams

Published in the United States of America by:
Creative Teaching Press, Inc.
P.O. Box 2723
Huntington Beach, CA 92647-0723

CTP 3233

Little Zebra is at the zoo.

What can Little Zebra do?

Zebra can zoom.

Zebra can zap!

Zebra can zigzag
on the path.

Little Zebra is at the zoo.

What can Little Zebra do?

"Z-z-z-z-z-z-z-z-z!"
Good night, Little Zebra!

Create your own book!

Make a list of all the z words you know. Use the words and your own illustrations to make a book titled *Little Zebra's Book of Z*. Decorate the cover with a zebra cut from zebra-striped foam paper (available at craft stores).

Words in *Little Zebra*

Initial Consonant: *z*	High-Frequency Words	Other
zebra	is	little
zoo	at	path
zoom	the	good night
zap	what	yawn
zigzag	can	
zingers	do	
z-z-z-z-z-z	on	